KID
DETECTIVES

THE PECULIAR AFFAIR OF CLOUDY WATER

Adam Bushnell
Illustrated by John Haslam

This story includes puzzles and questions. Answers can be found on page 31. You will also find a quiz on page 30 and a glossary on page 32.

WAYLAND

It was a sunny Sunday morning in spring, when Farah, Isla, Mohammad and Sam were headed to the bridge crossing the local river.
"I've never been fishing before," Sam said to his friends.
He was looking at the fishing rod, which he held like it was a dangerous animal.

"You'll love it!" laughed Farah.
"We'll show you how!" added Isla.
"Do I have to put maggots on the hook?" asked Sam.
"No," answered Mohammad. "We're using these instead."
He held out a tin of sweetcorn and small bits of cheese.
"Phew!" Sam said.

The four friends crossed the bridge that stretched over the river.
"This is our favourite spot," Isla announced as they looked down at the water.
Mohammad furrowed his brow as he looked at the river.

"That's not right," he said with his hands on his hips.
"It wasn't like this last year! Look," Farah gasped as she
showed the friends a photo on her phone.
"What's happened?" exclaimed Sam.

Spot the difference between then and now.

"I think we need to find out!" Farah said, making her way down towards the riverbank.

The others joined her and followed a trail of algae along the river.

"What's happened to the reeds?" asked Isla, alarmed.

"It's spring. There should be loads of cute ducklings ..." Sam said, looking up and down the river with a hand over his eyes.

There were dead fish floating on the surface of the brown murky water.
Drooping plants hung down the sides of the riverbank.
"Maybe something has got into the water and is killing everything!"
Isla said, sadly.
"It must be some kind of pollution," suggested Mohammad.
"But where is it coming from?" asked Sam.

WHAT IS POLLUTION?

Pollution is damage caused to water,
air or land by waste, chemicals or
other harmful substances.

"I think we need to tell someone about this," Isla said, grimly.
"Who do we know that could help? What sort of expert do we need?" asked Sam.
"Someone who knows about pollution," Farah suggested.
"I think my dad knows someone at the Department for the Environment. They'll know what to do!" exclaimed Mohammad.

The children raced over to Mohammad's house to tell his dad, Abdul. They showed him the pictures Farah had taken.
"It looks like water contamination. The river could be a danger to the community and could cause health issues. I'll report it to my friend at the Department for the Environment right away," Abdul said, shaking his head.

WHAT IS CONTAMINATION?

Contamination happens when something, such as water, contains unwanted or dangerous substances that make it dirty and unsafe to use.

A few days later, the children went down to the river with Abdul to meet with his friend who was collecting samples.

"You must not swim in rivers, kids. You can never be sure whether the water is clean. And ..."

Mohammad interrupted, "We know Dad. There might also be strong currents."

"You could get caught in pond weed, too," Sam added.
"Also, no going too close to the water's edge as you might fall in," Isla said with a nod.
As they neared the bridge, they noticed somebody wearing a protective suit and wellies. They were kneeling by the riverbank with water collection equipment next to them.

What sort of tools do you think are needed to collect samples safely?

"Hello old friend!" called Abdul with a wave.
The woman collecting the samples waved back.
"Hi gang, I'm Elise. I work for the Department for the Environment.
Thank you for reporting this."
"Do you know what it is?" asked Farah.

"It could be one of a few things," Elise explained. "It could be nutrient pollution from fertiliser and sewage ending up in a river. This can cause too much algae to grow. Surface water pollution is usually caused by an oil spill. Chemical pollution is when chemicals, such as pesticides from farms, leak into the water, destroying wildlife."

From what you can see in and around the river, what kind of pollution is affecting the river?

"We can actually do some tests right now. Do you want to help?" asked Elise.

The children nodded excitedly.

"You'll have to wear these gloves to protect your hands," she said as she handed out blue rubber gloves. Elise then gave them a sample bottle each and thin paper strips.

"What are these for?" asked Sam, holding up his strip of paper.
"This is an indicator. It's a substance that will change colour
depending on the pH of what it is dipped in. So dip it into the water
and in a few seconds it will change colour and show us how acidic
the water is," Elise explained.

WHAT IS PH?

PH stands for the power of
hydrogen. It is the scale used
to test how acidic or alkaline
something is.

The children dipped the strips, which all turned a bright red colour. "Here is the scale to compare the results to," Elise said as she handed Isla a colourful chart.

Take a look at the colour chart on page 17. What does the pH test tell us about the water?

"The reading tells me the pollution is definitely from chemicals. I'll needs to do further testing in my laboratory," said Elise shaking her head.
Elise then collected more samples in larger bottles, packed up her equipment and waved goodbye.

The next day, the children were in Isla's garden playing with her dog, Belle.

"Yesterday, Elise only tested the water," Isla said with a furrowed brow. "She didn't find out where the pollution was coming from."

"That's true," nodded Mohammad. "Do you think we should go back to investigate?"

"Definitely," said Farah firmly. "Maybe we can track down the source of the pollution."
The four friends went back to the river and followed the polluted water, walking upstream trying to find clues.

? Can you spot any clues that show where the pollution is coming from?

"Come and see! There's a lot more algae here!" Farah cried out. The four friends joined her further up the riverbank, by a field. "And look at that water running into the river from the field," Mohammad pointed out.

"The pollution must be coming from that farm!" Sam said, pointing to a farm further ahead.

"He's right," Mohammad said, nodding. "Let's stay here and watch the farm. Something is going on here."

The four friends sat on some soft grass and watched the farmer on the opposite bank. He was loading big bags of something into a tractor.

What could be causing the pollution?

As the farmer approached the end of the field, he saw the children watching him.

"Hey!" the farmer shouted. "What are you lot up to?"

"We're sorry to bother you," Sam said with a smile. "But we think your fertiliser is leaking into the river."

The farmer stomped over with a red face.
"What?" he asked with a grumpy expression.
"Your fertiliser is polluting the river," Isla explained. "Look."
The farmer saw the colour of the river, the withered plants
and the floating fish. His expression changed.

WHAT IS FERTILISER?

Fertiliser is chemical or natural
substance added to soil or land
to make plants grow well.

The children took the farmer along the riverbank to see how far his fertiliser had affected the plants and wildlife. As they neared the bridge, they saw Elise in her protective suit taking more samples.
"Hi Elise!" waved Mohammad.

"Hi kids!" Elise waved back. "Great to see you again."
"I'm very sorry to say this, but it appears to be all my fault," the farmer said with a flushed face.
"It's not just you," Elise explained. "The fertiliser factory behind your farm is leaking a strong chemical. I've already set up an investigation to check if they have the proper safety measures in place."

"What can I do?" asked the farmer.
"You could switch to a more environmentally friendly fertiliser,"
Elise explained. "It would also be good to create a field barrier by
planting trees and shrubs between your crops and the river. The
plants will act as a wall, stopping these harmful chemicals from
getting into the water."
"Fantastic!" replied the farmer.

Elise, the farmer and the four friends walked
back to the farmer's field. There, Elise
pointed to the place where the fertiliser was
leaking and suggested which plants were best
for creating a barrier.

The children then walked back towards the bridge.
"What else can we do to stop river pollution?" asked Mohammad.
"The best thing that you can do is to keep the environment clean.
You could organise litter clean-ups," Elise said with a wide smile.
"But there are lots of things that my department can do, such as
planting more trees, which help the whole ecosystem."

Over the next month, the four friends worked hard to help Elise's department.

They organised litter clean-ups, planted trees and made presentations to help raise awareness about river pollution. Slowly, the river returned to being the place they loved.

QUIZ

1. What is nutrient pollution?
a. something spilt on to the surface of the water.
b. chemicals in the water that shouldn't be there.
c. too many nutrients in the river.

2. What are the effects of chemical pollution in a river?
a. it destroys wildlife and makes water unsafe to drink.
b. it makes more plants grow.
c. it makes the river dry up.

3. What does the pH test do?
a. it shows pollution in the water.
b. it shows nutrients in the water.
c. it shows acidity in the water.

4. What does pH stand for?
a. the power of helium.
b. the power of hydrogen.
c. the power of hydrology.

5. What can be done to prevent fertiliser leaking into waterways?
a. we can build brick walls around fields.
b. we can plant trees and shrubs around fields.
c. we can place sandbags around fields.

Quiz answers: 1 c, 2 a, 3 c, 4 b, 5 b

ANSWERS

Page 5:
Then: the river water is clean, the plants are alive and there are healthy animals, such as the frog and heron.
Now: the river water is dirty, the plants are dead and the fish are dead.

Page 11:
There are two sets of tools needed to collect water samples safely. First, the protective equipment that includes clean rubber gloves, goggles, a mask, protective overalls and wellies. The second set of tools relate to collecting the samples, which includes sample bottles, labels and a pen, sealable storage bags to avoid spills and a box to carry the samples safely to the laboratory.

Page 13:
The dead plants and fish point towards chemical pollution. The green algae floating on the water's surface point to nutrient pollution.

Page 16:
The bright red colour refers to 1 on the colour chart, the most acidic colour on the scale.

Page 21:
The big bags that the farmer is carrying have spilled all over the ground. You can see a trail of dark green going from them into the river, indicating that the substance has leaked into the river.

Glossary

acidic having the chemical properties of an acid, a substance that can react with and sometimes break down other materials. Has a pH below 7

algae small plants that grow in water and do not have leaves or roots

alkaline having an effect or chemical behaviour opposite to an acid. Has a pH above 7

chemicals substances that are made up of tiny particles called atoms. Some are essential to life, such as water, some can be harmful if not used properly

ecosystem all the living things in an area and the way they affect each other and the environment

fertiliser a natural or chemical substance that is spread on the land to make plants grow well

nutrient any substance that plants or animals need in order to live and grow

oil spill an accident in which oil has come out of a ship or pipe and caused pollution

pesticide a chemical substance used to kill insects that harm crops

sewage water and waste material, such as wee and poo that should be carried away in sewers

substance a particular kind of matter with specific properties

upstream moving in the opposite direction of the flow of a river

First published in Great Britain in 2024 by Wayland
Copyright © Hodder and Stoughton, 2024
All rights reserved

Editor: Elise Short
Designer: Lisa Peacock
Science Consultant: Peter Riley,
science author and educator

HB ISBN: 978 1 5263 2488 7
PB ISBN: 978 1 5263 2489 4

Printed and bound in China

Wayland, an imprint of
Hachette Children's Group
Part of Hodder and Stoughton
Carmelite House
50 Victoria Embankment
London EC4Y 0DZ
An Hachette UK Company

www.hachette.co.uk
www.hachettechildrens.co.uk

FSC
www.fsc.org
MIX
Paper from
responsible sources
FSC® C104740